ROCK & POP

Grade 3

DRUMS

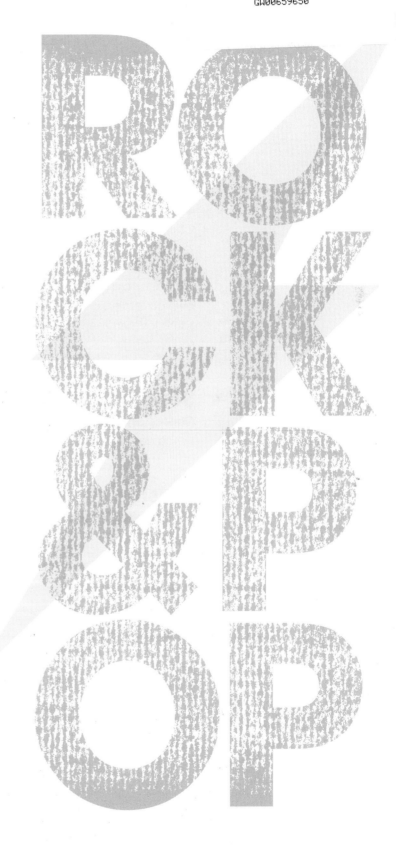

GW00659650

TRINITY
COLLEGE LONDON

THE EXAM AT A GLANCE

For your Rock & Pop exam you will need to perform a set of **three songs** and one of the **Session skills** assessments, either **Playback** or **Improvising**. You can choose the order in which you play your set-list.

Song 1

Choose a song from this book

OR from www.trinityrock.com

Song 2

Choose a different song from this book

OR from www.trinityrock.com

OR perform a song you have chosen yourself: this could be your own cover version or a song you have written. It should be at the same level as the songs in this book. See the website for detailed requirements.

Song 3: Technical focus

Choose one of the Technical focus songs from this book, which cover three specific technical elements.

Session skills

Choose either **Playback** or **Improvising**.

When you are preparing for your exam please check on **www.trinityrock.com** for the most up-to-date information and requirements as these can change from time to time.

CONTENTS

Songs	**Chain Of Fools**	**4**
	Creep	**6**
	Sunshine Of Your Love	**7**
	Natural Blues	**8**
Technical focus songs	**All Day And All Of The Night**	**9**
	John Barleycorn	**12**
About the songs	**Chain Of Fools**	**14**
	Creep	**15**
	Sunshine Of Your Love	**16**
	Natural Blues	**17**
	All Day And All Of The Night	**18**
	John Barleycorn	**19**
Session skills	**Playback**	**20**
	Improvising	**22**
Help pages	**Choosing a song for your exam**	**23**
	Writing your own song	**24**
	Playing in a band	**25**
	Playing with backing tracks	**26**
	Copyright in a song	**26**
	Drum notation guide	**27**

Each song has two backing tracks: the first includes a click track to play along with, the second omits the click track.

Trinity College London's Rock & Pop syllabus and supporting publications have been devised and produced in association with Faber Music and Peters Edition London.

Trinity College London
Registered office:
89 Albert Embankment
London SE1 7TP UK
T + 44 (0)20 7820 6100
F + 44 (0)20 7820 6161
E music@trinitycollege.co.uk
www.trinitycollege.co.uk

Registered in the UK. Company no. 02683033
Charity no. 1014792
Patron HRH The Duke of Kent KG

Copyright © 2012 Trinity College London
First published in 2012 by Trinity College London

Third impression, January 2013

Cover and book design by Chloë Alexander
Brand development by Andy Ashburner @ Caffeinehit (www.caffeinehit.com)
Photographs courtesy of Rex Features Limited.
Printed in England by Caligraving Ltd

Audio produced, mixed and mastered by Tom Fleming
Drums arranged by George Double
Backing tracks arranged by Tom Fleming
Musicians
Vocals: Bo Walton, Brendan Reilly & Alison Symons
Keyboards: Oliver Weeks
Guitar: Tom Fleming
Bass: Ben Hillyard
Drums: George Double
Studio Engineer: Joel Davies www.thelimehouse.com

All rights reserved

ISBN: 978-0-85736-248-3

TRACK 1 demo
TRACK 2-3 backing
2 with click
3 without click

SONGS CHAIN OF FOOLS

Aretha Franklin
Words and Music by Donald Covay

Motown   *2 bars count-in*

♩ = 116

Intro

vocal cue
"Chain, chain, chain..."

vocal cue
"For five long years..."
fill

Verse

cont. sim.   (4)

vocal cue
"You got me where you want me..."
(8)   *fill*

(12)

22

vocal cue
"Chain, chain, chain..."

Chorus

26

f

Middle

voice and kit

vocal cue
"You told me to leave you alone…"

30
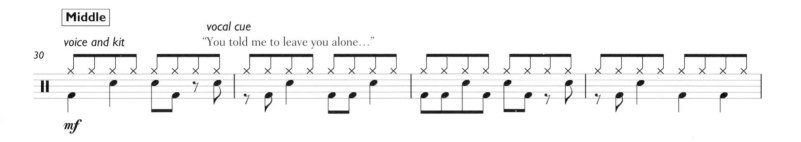
mf

vocal cue
"I'm added to your"

34

vocal cue
"Chain, chain, chain..."

Chorus

39
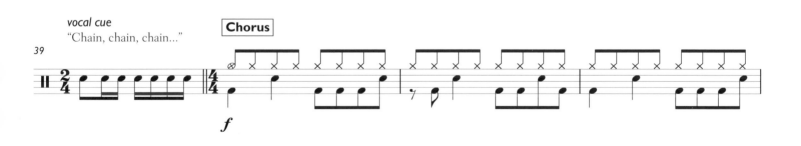
f

Ride

43

SONGS CREEP

TRACK 4 demo
TRACK 5-6 backing
5 with click
6 without click

Radiohead

Words and Music by Thomas Yorke, Jonathan Greenwood, Colin Greenwood, Edward O'Brien, Philip Selway, Albert Hammond and Mike Hazelwood

♩ = 96 **Indie Rock Ballad** *2 bars count-in*

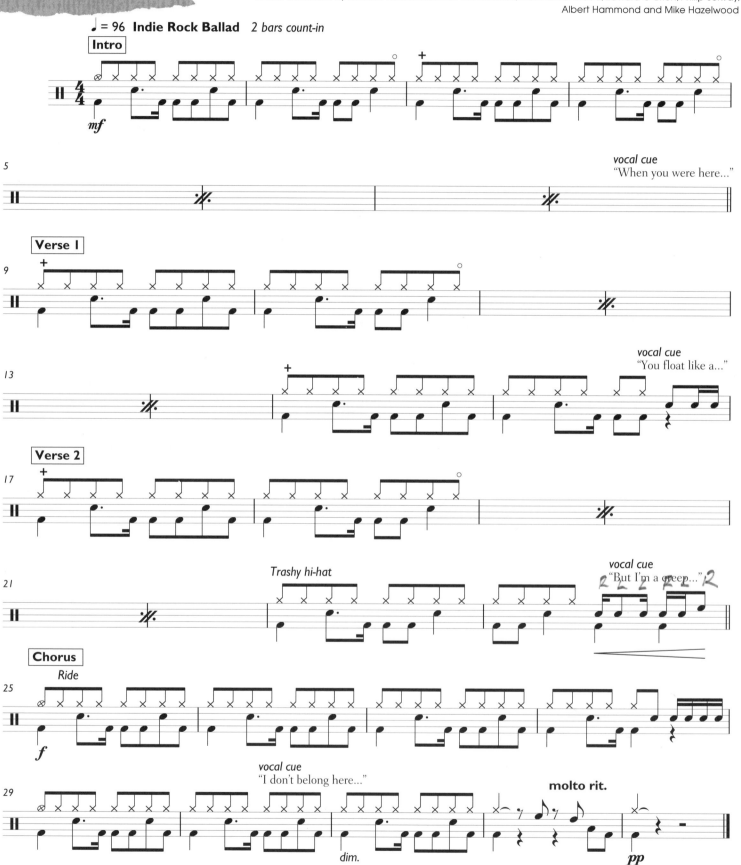

www.trinityrock.com

SONGS SUNSHINE OF YOUR LOVE

TRACK 7 demo

TRACK 8-9 backing
8 with click
9 without click

Cream

Words and Music by Jack Bruce, Peter Brown and Eric Clapton

SONGS NATURAL BLUES

Moby
Words and Music by Vera Hall, Alan Lomax and Moby

ALL DAY AND ALL OF THE NIGHT

In your exam, you will be assessed on the following technical elements:

1 Dynamic range

There are three dynamic marking in this song. These tell you how loudly or quietly to play. Look out for these markings:

- *mf* (*mezzo forte* = quite loud)
- *f* (*forte* = loud)
- *ff* (*fortissimo* = very loud)

Look out for passages where the dynamics change suddenly and make sure that the contrast is clear.

There is a *crescendo* (———) in bars 33–34. Practise this until you can make a smooth and gradual dynamic change.

2 Improvised fills

'All Day And All Of The Night' has 'fill' marked at bars 20, 22, 40 and 42, and 'big fill' at bar 36. Judging what, how much and how loud to play fills is one of the greatest challenges to any drummer. You should always think about the musical event that you are moving towards. If it is a fill that leads into a very full, strong chorus you should probably play a much more dramatic fill than if it is only a small transitional fill.

3 Playing ♪ evenly

Bars 12, 16, 36 and 43 contain ♪ fills on the snare drum. These should be played as single strokes which, at 136bpm, can be a challenge – particularly when striving for even and consistent sound. Practise your single stroke technique to keep the rhythms flowing. Both sticks should rise to the same height: you could also think about striking the playing surface of the snare in a similar spot with both sticks for a really focused, consistent sound.

TECHNICAL FOCUS SONGS

TRACK 13
demo

TRACK 14-15
backing
14 with click
15 without click

ALL DAY AND ALL OF THE NIGHT

The Kinks

Words and Music by Ray Davies

♩ = 136 **Rock** *2 bars count-in*

Intro

Guitar riff   *mf*

Verse

vocal cue
"I'm not content..."

vocal cue
"The only time I feel alright..."

Trashy hats

f

Chorus I

vocal cue
"Girl, I want to be with you..."

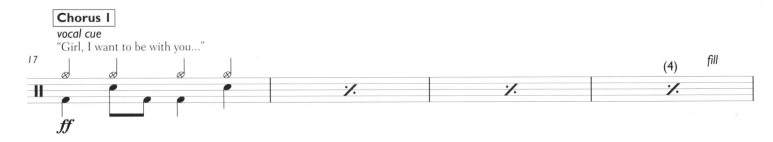

ff   *(4)*   *fill*

Guitar solo

Trashy hats

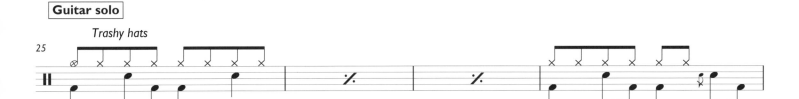

Tight hats

(4)

mf

Bass break

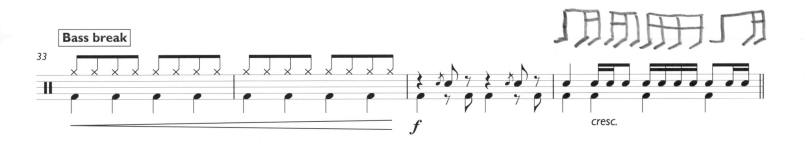

f　　*cresc.*

Chorus 2

vocal cue
"Girl, I want to be with you..."

(4)　　*fill*

f

vocal cue
"...all of the night."

fill　　*fill*

JOHN BARLEYCORN

In your exam, you will be assessed on the following technical elements:

1 Hand/foot co-ordination

During the grooves, the snare often plays a ♪ note between ♪ notes on the hi-hat. This technique should be practised slowly before playing with the backing track. Try to listen in two ways: firstly to how the snare rhythm works independently as a separate rhythm; and secondly, to how it fits in with the other sounds, working in combination with them.

2 Rolls

Verse 1 (bars 9–16) features ♩ rolls. At this tempo, these rolls should be played as either 9-stroke rolls (♪ division) or as buzzed ♪ notes. Make sure that your main stroke speed is ♪, and that you are pressing the sticks into the playing surface, letting them bounce to fill out the sound smoothly.

3 Improvised fills

There are fills at bars 2, 28 and 30. Judging what, how much and how loud to play fills is one of the greatest challenges to any drummer. You should always think about the musical event that you are moving towards. If it is a fill that leads into a very full, strong chorus you should probably play a much more dramatic fill than if it is only a small transitional fill.

TECHNICAL FOCUS SONGS

BAND OPTION

JOHN BARLEYCORN

Traditional
Words and Music Trad.

TRACK 16 · demo
TRACK 17-18 · backing
17 with click
18 without click

CHAIN OF FOOLS

Aretha Franklin

Aretha Franklin, from Memphis, Tennessee, is the daughter of a Baptist preacher. She started out as a gospel singer in her father's church, learning from some of the great gospel singers of the time, including Mahalia Jackson. She signed to the famous soul music label Atlantic Records in 1966.

With her expressive, gospel-tinged vocals, Aretha Franklin had an impressive run of soul hits in the late 1960s, including 'I Never Loved A Man' and 'I Say A Little Prayer'. She is often referred to as the Queen of Soul. 'Chain Of Fools' was released in 1967 as a single and appeared on many of her later albums.

PERFORMANCE · HINTS & TIPS ·

'Chain Of Fools' uses the snare on the off-beat ♪ – this is often found in soul music. You should think about phrasing in two-bar phrases – the missing bass drum on the first beat of the second bar in each phrase makes it feel like a continuation of the previous bar.

The drums enter in bar 2, so you will need to count bar 1 carefully to make sure that you come in exactly on the first beat of bar 2. Make sure that you are ready for the time signature change at bar 39. This fill leads neatly into the chorus.

The final ♪ of the song has a symbol which looks like a tie leading from it. This is known as an *l.v.* (*laissez vibrer*) mark and means the note should ring on. More commonly this technique, where the end of a phrase comes on beat 4+, is known as a push. This final note works best as a crash with bass drum beneath.

'But *I* found *out* I'm *just* a *link* in *your* chain'

CREEP

Radiohead

'Creep' was a surprise worldwide hit for Radiohead in 1993. It was originally released as a single and then again on Radiohead's early album *Pablo Honey*. The self-loathing lyrics tell of an unsuccessful crush – hitting an angst-ridden nerve that clearly many can identify with.

The song opens with Thom Yorke's vulnerable-sounding voice against a sparse background of guitar and drums. This quiet, restrained opening builds up through a long *crescendo* to a magnificent climax with wailing falsetto and distorted guitars, falling back down again to the bittersweet plaintive sounds of the opening.

The challenge in this song is to master the foot/hand independence. There is a ♩♩ figure in the main groove, with the bass drum ♪ placed between the hi-hat notes. Work on this pattern slowly at first: this will help develop independent footwork.

The use of a slightly open 'trashy' hi-hat sound at bar 23 forms a link with the much more open, resonant ride cymbal in the chorus. Judge how much to open the hi-hats, filling the sound out and building to the chorus.

'Creep' is marked *molto rit.* in bars 32–33. This is short for *molto ritenuto*, which means that you should slow down a lot – but make sure the last bar is co-ordinated with the guitar chord.

'*I don't belong here*'

SUNSHINE OF YOUR LOVE

Cream

'Sunshine Of Your Love' is one of several classic songs on Cream's highly influential blues-rock album *Disraeli Gears* (1967). The band comprised Eric Clapton (guitar), Jack Bruce (bass) and Ginger Baker (drums) – each of them highly accomplished rock musicians, coming together as probably the first rock supergroup. They started as a blues revival band but their style gradually evolved into hard rock. They were famous for their live performances and long improvised solos.

'Sunshine Of Your Love' opens with one of the most famous riffs ever recorded.

PERFORMANCE HINTS & TIPS

In many rock and pop songs, it is common to stress the second and fourth beat of the bar on snare. 'Sunshine Of Your Love' is different – the stresses are firmly on beats one and three. The patterns played by the drums are very unusual too, mainly focusing on 'darker' drum sounds rather than brighter metal ones.

The drums enter on the second beat of bar 2. You will need to count carefully – it will also help to listen to the guitar riff.

In the chorus, aim for perfect alignment of the ♩ ♪ rhythm: don't play the second note too early. The chorus also features flams. Remember that flams can be thought of as single sounds even though they have two distinct playing actions. Keep the stick that plays the grace note closer to the playing surface than the higher second stick.

On playing the chorus for the second time (bar 43), there is an instruction to 'ad lib. fill on repeat', which means you are free to make up your own fill in bars 43–44, rather than play what has been notated.

This song is also in the guitar and bass books, so you can get together and play it in a band.

'I'll *be* with *you* when *the* stars start *falling*'

NATURAL BLUES

Moby

Moby lives in New York. He is a DJ, singer-songwriter and performer (on keyboard, guitar, bass and drums). 'Natural Blues' comes from his dance music album *Play* (1999). It is characterised by extensive use of samples, loops and layered textures.

The tracks on *Play* were written and played by Moby and then recorded and mixed at his home studio. The equipment used includes synthesisers, a sampler and a Roland TR909 drum machine. The Roland TR drum machine was one of the first to have programmable rhythms.

'Natural Blues' samples 'Trouble So Hard', by American folk singers Vera Hall and Dock Reed.

This song uses ♪ notes on the hi-hat in the groove. This is often called a '16-beat' pattern, as ♪ notes are also known as "sixteenth notes". These notes should be played as single strokes, phrasing them clearly in groups of four.

In bar 17 onwards the floor tom pattern uses accents (>). Make the accented notes louder and place them carefully.

At bar 36 there is a ruff. This is a rudiment with three grace notes preceding the main note. The sticking here should be r l r **L** or l r l **R**: whichever you prefer. Try to aim for a very fluid technique on the ruff, arriving on the main note with a burst of energy.

'My *soul* got *happy* and *stayed* all *day*'

ALL DAY AND ALL OF THE NIGHT

The Kinks

The Kinks were one of the most influential bands of the 1960s. A four-piece London Mod band, they produced short punchy songs, often with high quality lyrics written by their singer Ray Davies. Like many British bands of that time, they began as an R&B group but their style changed over their long career.

The Kinks had a string of hit singles during the 1960s, including 'All Day And All Of The Night', which is built upon a simple sliding power chord riff.

This song should sound big and bold. The backbeats (beats two and four) should be very strong: enjoy them, but make sure that you follow the dynamic markings as well.

The drums enter with a pick-up at the end of bar 2. You will need to count the first two bars carefully. It will also help to listen to the opening guitar riff.

'All Day And All Of The Night' uses both 'trashy hats' and 'tight hats'. Pressing tightly on the hi-hat pedal results in a tight sound, whereas releasing the foot pressure slightly allows the hi-hat cymbals to vibrate more. This 'splashy' sound is a really effective way of filling the music out – if used tastefully.

This song is also in the guitar, bass, vocals and keyboards books, so you can get together and play it in a band.

'Girl, *I want* to be *with* you. *all of* the *time*'

www.trinityrock.com

JOHN BARLEYCORN

Traditional

'John Barleycorn' is an English folk ballad with a long history dating back to the 16th century. This song – like all songs in the ballad tradition – tells a story. Nobody is really sure who John Barleycorn was, but one idea is that the name represents alcoholic drinks made from barley – a type of corn. There have been many versions of this song, by both folk singers and rock musicians. The 1960s rock band Traffic even named one of their best-selling albums after it – *John Barleycorn Must Die*.

PERFORMANCE · HINTS & TIPS ·

'John Barleycorn' is made up of several sections – intro, verses, link and outro – each with different drum rhythms. There are also opportunities for you to improvise in the fills.

Note the dynamic markings in the intro and the link. Both sections open ***mf*** (*mezzo forte* = moderately loud) and then change to ***mp*** (*mezzo piano* = moderately quiet). Make sure that there is a clear difference between ***mf*** and ***mp***.

There are notes above the stave in the final bar of this song. This is a cue, which shows the main rhythmic pattern of the band. This rhythm should be incorporated into the final bar.

This song is also in the guitar, bass, vocals and keyboards books, so you can get together and play it in a band.

'These *three* men *made* a solemn vow'

PLAYBACK

For your exam, you can choose either Playback or Improvising (see page 22).
If you choose Playback, you will be asked to play some music you have not seen
or heard before.

In the exam, you will be given the song chart and the examiner will play a recording
of the music. You will hear several two-bar or four-bar phrases on the recording:
you should play each of them straight back in turn. There's a rhythm track going
throughout, which helps you keep in time. There should not be any gaps in the music.

In the exam you will have two chances to play with the recording:
- First time – for practice
- Second time – for assessment.

You should listen to the audio, copying what you hear; you can also read the music.
Here are some practice song charts which are also on the CD in this book.

Don't forget that the Playback test can include requirements which may not be
shown in these examples, including those from earlier grades. Check the parameters
at www.trinityrock.com to prepare for everything which might come up in your exam.

'I really *like*
the *way*
music *looks* on *paper.*
It *looks* like *art*
to *me*'

Steve Vai

Practice playback 1

Practice playback 2

IMPROVISING

For your exam, you can choose either Playback (see page 20), or Improvising. If you choose to improvise, you will be asked to improvise over a backing track that you haven't heard before in a specified style.

In the exam, you will be given a song chart and the examiner will play a recording of the backing track. The backing track consists of a passage of music played on a loop. You should improvise a drum groove to it.

In the exam you will have two chances to play with the recording:
*   First time – for practice
*   Second time – for assessment.

Here are some improvising charts for practice which are also on the CD in this book.

Don't forget that the Improvising test can include requirements which may not be shown in these examples, including those from earlier grades. Check the parameters at www.trinityrock.com to prepare for everything which might come up in your exam.

Practice improvisation 1

$\quad$ = 60 **Blues** (swung quavers)

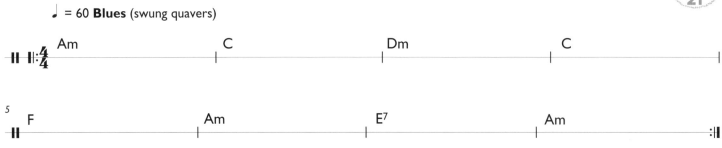

Practice improvisation 2

$\quad$ = 80 **Ballad**

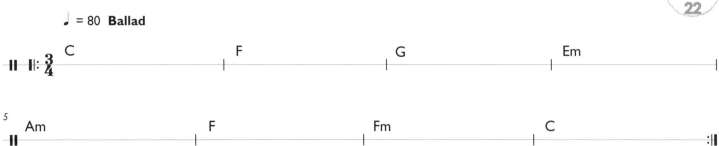

CHOOSING A SONG FOR YOUR EXAM

There are lots of options to help you choose your three songs for the exam.
For Songs 1 and 2, you can choose a song which is:

- from this book
- from www.trinityrock.com

Or for Song 2 you can choose a song which is:

- sheet music from a printed or online source
- your own arrangement of a song or a song you have written yourself (see page 24).

You can play the song unaccompanied or with a backing track (minus the drum part). If you like, you can create a backing track yourself (or with friends), or you could add your own vocals – or both.

For Grade 3, the song should last between one-and-a-half and three-and-a-half minutes, and the level of difficulty should be similar to your other songs. When choosing a song, think about:

- Does it work on my instrument?
- Are there any technical elements that are too difficult for me? (If so, perhaps save it for when you do the next grade.)
- Do I enjoy playing it?
- Does it work with my other pieces to create a good set-list?

See www.trinityrock.com for further information and advice on choosing your own song.

SHEET MUSIC

You must always bring an original copy of the book or a download sheet with email certificate for each song you perform in the exam. If you choose to write your own song you must provide the examiner with a copy of the sheet music. Your music can be:

- a lead sheet with lyrics, chords and melody line
- a chord chart with lyrics
- a full score using conventional staff notation
- see page 24 for details on presenting a song you have written yourself.

The title of the song and your name should be on the sheet music.

WRITING YOUR OWN SONG

You can play a song that you have written yourself for one of the choices in your exam. For Grade 3, the song should last between one-and-a-half and three-and-a-half minutes. It is sometimes difficult to know where to begin, however. Here are some suggestions for starting points:

- **A rhythm**: A short repeated rhythm will often underpin an entire song. Start by writing a couple of short rhythms here:

- **A riff**: A riff is a short rhythm which is repeated over and over. A short repeated riff will often underpin an entire song. Write a couple of riffs here:

WRITING YOUR SONG DOWN

Rock and pop music is often written as a **lead sheet** with the lyrics (if there are any), chords and a melody line.

- As a drummer, you may want to write your part using **drum notation**, used for the songs in this book. There is a guide to this notation on page 27.

- You can, if you prefer, use a **graph** or **table** to represent your music, as long as it is clear to anyone else (including the examiner) how the song goes.

- **Instruments**: Which instruments will play your song? You could use keyboard, bass and drums, or you could add vocals, guitar and any other instruments.

There are plenty of other ways of starting: perhaps with a melody, chord sequence or a lyric, for example.

You will also need to consider the **structure** of your song (verse and chorus, 12-bar blues, and so on) and the **style** it is in (blues, hard rock, etc.).

There are many choices to be made – which is why writing a song is such a rewarding thing to do.

PLAYING IN A BAND

Playing in a band is exciting: it can be a lot of fun and, as with everything, the more you do it, the easier it gets. It is very different from playing on your own. Everyone contributes to the overall sound: the most important skill you need to develop is listening.

For a band to sound good, the players need to be 'together' – that mainly means keeping in time with each other, but also playing at the same volume, and with the same kind of feeling.

Your relationship with the other band members is also important. Talk with them about the music you play, the music you like, and what you'd like the band to achieve short-term and long-term.

Band rehearsals are important – you should not be late, tired or distracted by your mobile phone! Being positive makes a huge difference. Try to create a friendly atmosphere in rehearsals so that everybody feels comfortable trying out new things. Don't worry about making mistakes: that is what rehearsals are for.

'All Day And All Of The Night' (page 10) and 'John Barleycorn' (page 13) are arranged for band. You will find parts for vocals, guitar, bass and keyboards in the other Trinity Rock & Pop Grade 3 books or available online. There are also parts for 'Sunshine Of Your Love' in Trinity Rock & Pop Grade 3 Guitar and Bass books. Trinity offers exams for groups of musicians at various levels. The songs arranged for bands are ideal to include as part of a set-list for these exams. Have a look at the website for more details.

HINTS AND TIPS

- Record your practice sessions and listen carefully to the recordings. Which sections worked well and which had problems? How will you improve the sections with problems?

- In some songs you will play a supporting role; at other times you may take more of a lead. In both cases you need to listen to the overall group as well as to your own part. Be aware of how you affect the sound – every player should make their own distinct contribution to the overall sound.

- Nothing beats the thrill of performing live in front of an audience. Organise a gig for a few friends. It can be a small gig in someone's house – the important thing is to get used to playing in front of other people. Gigs can be nerve-wracking at first, but try to relax and enjoy them.

PLAYING WITH BACKING TRACKS

The CD contains demos and backing tracks of all the songs in the book.
The additional songs at www.trinityrock.com also come with demos and backing tracks.

- In your exam, you should perform with the backing track, or you can create your own (see below).
- The backing tracks begin with a click track, which sets the tempo and helps you start accurately.
- Be careful to set the balance between the volume of the backing track and your instrument.
- Listen carefully to the backing track to ensure you are playing in time.

If you are creating your own backing track here are some further tips:
- Make sure the sound quality is of a good standard.
- Think carefully about the instruments/sounds you are putting on the backing track.
- Avoid copying what you are playing on the backing track – it should support not duplicate.
- Do you need to include a click track at the beginning?

COPYRIGHT IN A SONG

If you are a singer or songwriter it is important to know about copyright. When someone writes a song or creates an arrangement they own the copyright (sometimes called 'the rights') to that version. The copyright means that other people cannot copy it, sell it, perform it in a concert, make it available online or record it without the owner's permission or the appropriate licence. When you write a song you automatically own the copyright to it, which means that other people cannot copy your work. But just as importantly, you cannot copy other people's work, or perform it in public without their permission or the appropriate licence.

Points to remember
- You can create a cover version of a song for an exam or other non-public performance.
- You cannot record your cover version and make your recording available to others (by copying it or uploading it to a website) without the appropriate licence.

- You own the copyright of your own original song, which means that no one is allowed to copy it.
- You cannot copy someone else's song without their permission or the appropriate licence.
- If you would like to use somebody else's words in your own song you must check if they are in copyright and, if so, we recommend you confirm with the author that they are happy for the words to be used as lyrics.
- Materials protected by copyright can normally be used as lyrics in our examinations as these are private performances under copyright law. The examiner may ask you the name of the original author in the exam.
- When you present your own song to the examiner, make sure you include the title, the names of any writers and the source of your lyrics.

HELP PAGES

DRUM NOTATION GUIDE

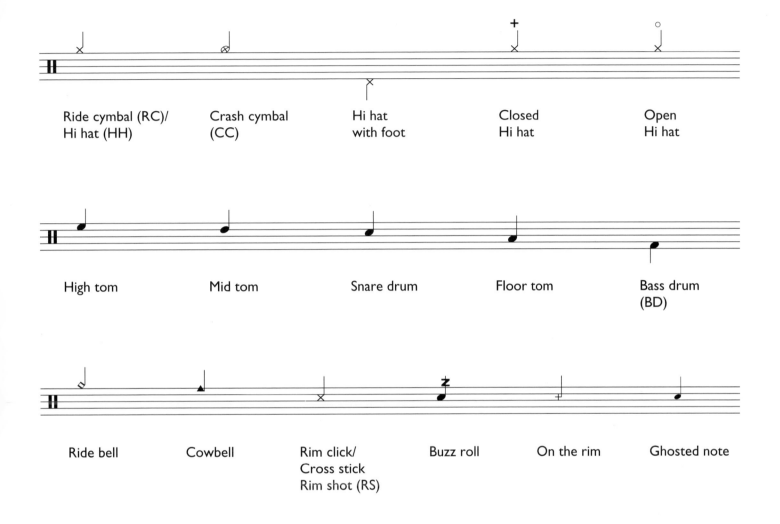

Ride cymbal (RC)/
Hi hat (HH)

Crash cymbal
(CC)

Hi hat
with foot

Closed
Hi hat

Open
Hi hat

High tom

Mid tom

Snare drum

Floor tom

Bass drum
(BD)

Ride bell

Cowbell

Rim click/
Cross stick
Rim shot (RS)

Buzz roll

On the rim

Ghosted note

ALSO AVAILABLE

Trinity College London Rock & Pop examinations 2012-2017 are also available for:

Bass Initial
ISBN: 978-0-85736-227-8

Bass Grade 1
ISBN: 978-0-85736-228-5

Bass Grade 2
ISBN: 978-0-85736-229-2

Bass Grade 3
ISBN: 978-0-85736-230-8

Bass Grade 4
ISBN: 978-0-85736-231-5

Bass Grade 5
ISBN: 978-0-85736-232-2

Bass Grade 6
ISBN: 978-0-85736-233-9

Bass Grade 7
ISBN: 978-0-85736-234-6

Bass Grade 8
ISBN: 978-0-85736-235-3

Drums Initial
ISBN: 978-0-85736-245-2

Drums Grade 1
ISBN: 978-0-85736-246-9

Drums Grade 2
ISBN: 978-0-85736-247-6

Drums Grade 3
ISBN: 978-0-85736-248-3

Drums Grade 4
ISBN: 978-0-85736-249-0

Drums Grade 5
ISBN: 978-0-85736-250-6

Drums Grade 6
ISBN: 978-0-85736-251-3

Drums Grade 7
ISBN: 978-0-85736-252-0

Drums Grade 8
ISBN: 978-0-85736-253-7

Guitar Initial
ISBN: 978-0-85736-218-6

Guitar Grade 1
ISBN: 978-0-85736-219-3

Guitar Grade 2
ISBN: 978-0-85736-220-9

Guitar Grade 3
ISBN: 978-0-85736-221-6

Guitar Grade 4
ISBN: 978-0-85736-222-3

Guitar Grade 5
ISBN: 978-0-85736-223-0

Guitar Grade 6
ISBN: 978-0-85736-224-7

Guitar Grade 7
ISBN: 978-0-85736-225-4

Guitar Grade 8
ISBN: 978-0-85736-226-1

Keyboards Initial
ISBN: 978-0-85736-236-0

Keyboards Grade 1
ISBN: 978-0-85736-237-7

Keyboards Grade 2
ISBN: 978-0-85736-238-4

Keyboards Grade 3
ISBN: 978-0-85736-239-1

Keyboards Grade 4
ISBN: 978-0-85736-240-7

Keyboards Grade 5
ISBN: 978-0-85736-241-4

Keyboards Grade 6
ISBN: 978-0-85736-242-1

Keyboards Grade 7
ISBN: 978-0-85736-243-8

Keyboards Grade 8
ISBN: 978-0-85736-244-5

Vocals Initial
ISBN: 978-0-85736-254-4

Vocals Grade 1
ISBN: 978-0-85736-255-1

Vocals Grade 2
ISBN: 978-0-85736-256-8

Vocals Grade 3
ISBN: 978-0-85736-257-5

Vocals Grade 4
ISBN: 978-0-85736-258-2

Vocals Grade 5
ISBN: 978-0-85736-259-9

Vocals Grade 6 (female voice)
ISBN: 978-0-85736-263-6

Vocals Grade 6 (male voice)
ISBN: 978-0-85736-260-5

Vocals Grade 7 (female voice)
ISBN: 978-0-85736-264-3

Vocals Grade 7 (male voice)
ISBN: 978-0-85736-261-2

Vocals Grade 8 (female voice)
ISBN: 978-0-85736-265-0

Vocals Grade 8 (male voice)
ISBN: 978-0-85736-262-9